You are never too big to read books.

You are never too small to read books.

In fact, you are just right.

You can do it!

You can read this book and begin

Cover Illustration from *If You Give a Mouse a Cookie* by Laura Numeroff. Illustrated by Felicia Bond. Illustrations copyright © 1985 by Felicia Bond. Reprinted by permission of Harper & Row, Publishers, Inc.

Acknowledgments appear on page 132.

Printed in the U.S.A.

ISBN: 0-395-51914-4

FGHIJ-VH-9987654321

Too Big

Senior Author
John J. Pikulski

*Senior Coordinating
Author*
J. David Cooper

*Senior Consulting
Author*
William K. Durr

Coordinating Authors
Kathryn H. Au
M. Jean Greenlaw
Marjorie Y. Lipson
Susan Page
Sheila W. Valencia
Karen K. Wixson

Authors
Rosalinda B. Barrera
Ruth P. Bunyan
Jacqueline L. Chaparro
Jacqueline C. Comas
Alan N. Crawford
Robert L. Hillerich
Timothy G. Johnson
Jana M. Mason
Pamela A. Mason
William E. Nagy
Joseph S. Renzulli
Alfredo Schifini

Senior Advisor
Richard C. Anderson

Advisors
Christopher J. Baker
Charles Peters

HOUGHTON MIFFLIN COMPANY   BOSTON
Atlanta   Dallas   Geneva, Illinois   Palo Alto   Princeton   Toronto

8

Animal Friends

BOOK 1

12

Who Is Tapping At My Window?
by A. G. Deming

30

Morning On the Farm
a traditional song

41

City Pets
a photo essay

48

Dear Zoo
by Rod Campbell

POETRY

46

The Lost Cat
by Shel Silverstein

47

Notice
by David McCord

67

At The Zoo
by Myra Cohn Livingston

READ ALONG BOOK

Skip to My Lou
retold and illustrated by
Nadine Bernard Westcott

70

I and it!

BOOK 2

74

Monster and the Baby
by Virginia Mueller

89

I Wish I Could Fly
by Ron Maris

115

And So Can I!
by Bill Gillham

POETRY

88

The Wrong Start
by Marchette Chute

110

Jump or Jiggle
by Evelyn Beyer

112

I Speak, I Say, I Talk
by Arnold L. Shapiro

READ ALONG BOOK

I Can't Get My Turtle to Move
by Elizabeth Lee O'Donnell

Animal

Animal friends are everywhere! Not just in zoos, forests, and pet shops—but in books, too. You will read about many animal friends in these stories and poems. Here come the animals!

Friends

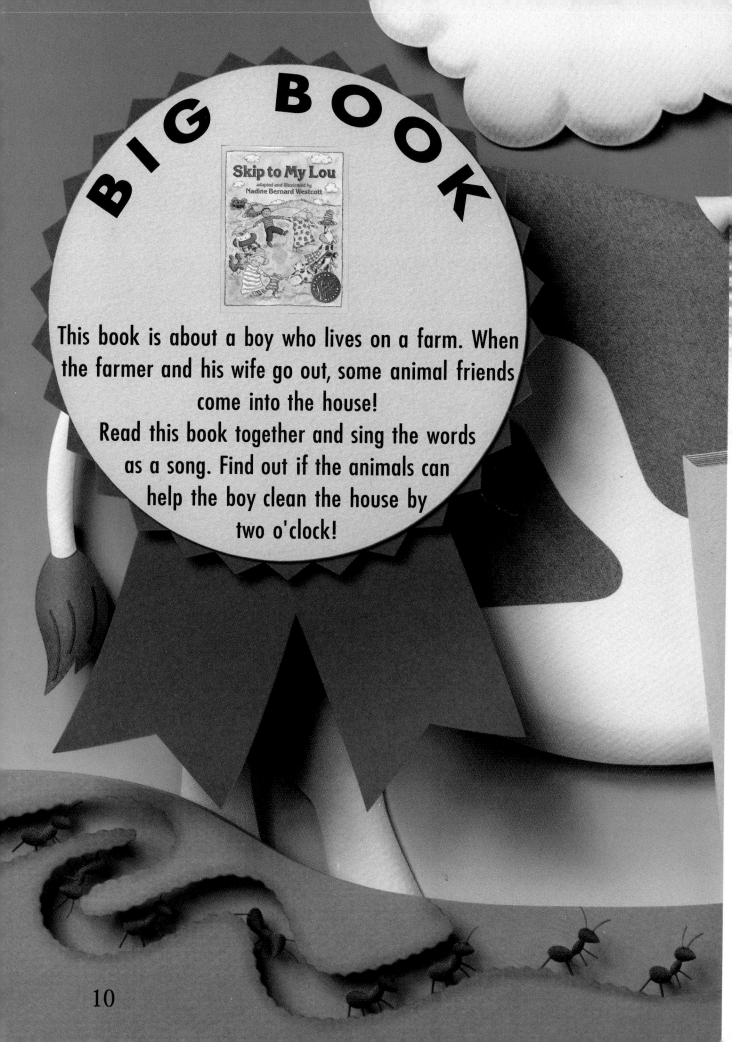

BIG BOOK

Skip to My Lou
adapted and illustrated by
Nadine Bernard Westcott

This book is about a boy who lives on a farm. When the farmer and his wife go out, some animal friends come into the house!
Read this book together and sing the words as a song. Find out if the animals can help the boy clean the house by two o'clock!

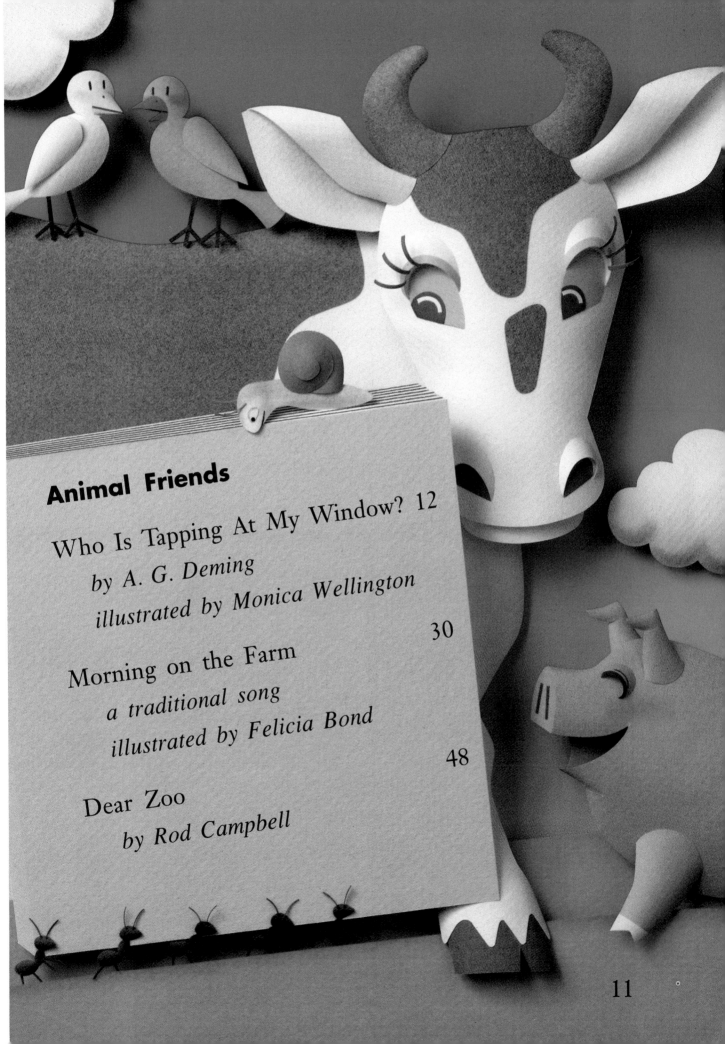

Animal Friends

Who Is Tapping At My Window? 12
   by A. G. Deming
      illustrated by Monica Wellington

Morning on the Farm   30
   a traditional song
      illustrated by Felicia Bond

Dear Zoo   48
   by Rod Campbell

11

Who Is Tapping

by A. G. Deming
pictures by Monica Wellington

At My Window?

Who is tapping at my window?

"It's not I," said the cat.

"It's not I," said the rat.

"It's not I," said the wren.

"It's not I," said the hen.

"It's not I," said the fox.

"It's not I," said the ox.

"It's not I," said the loon.

"It's not I," said the raccoon.

"It's not I," said the cony.

"It's not I," said the pony.

"It's not I," said the dog.

"It's not I," said the frog.

"It's not I," said the bear.

"It's not I," said the hare.

Who is tapping at my window?

"It is I," said the rain,

"tapping at your windowpane."

Animal Pictures

You have just read about some animal friends. Which one did you like best? Where could this animal go when it rains?

Draw a picture to show where the animal might go.

Meet the
ILLUSTRATOR

Monica Wellington has always loved to draw. She went to art school to study drawing. One day, Ms. Wellington was reading a very old poetry book. She found A. G. Deming's poem "Who Is Tapping At My Window?" She liked the poem so much that she drew pictures for it and made it into a storybook.

♪ Morning on the Farm ♪

A Traditional Song · illustrated by Felicia Bond

When sheep get up in the morning,
They always say, "Good day."

When sheep get up in the morning,
They always say, "Good day."

"Baa, baa, baa, baa,"
That is what they say, they say.

"Baa, baa, baa, baa,"
That is what they say.

When dogs get up in the morning,
They always say, "Good day."

When dogs get up in the morning,
They always say, "Good day."

"Bow–wow–wow–wow,"
That is what they say, they say.

"Bow–wow–wow–wow,"
That is what they say.

When ducks get up in the morning,
They always say, "Good day."

When ducks get up in the morning,
They always say, "Good day."

"Quack, quack! Quack, quack!"
That is what they say, they say.

"Quack, quack! Quack, quack!"
That is what they say.

35

When cats get up in the morning,
They always say, "Good day."

When cats get up in the morning,
They always say, "Good day."

"Meow, meow, meow, meow,"
That is what they say, they say.

"Meow, meow, meow, meow,"
That is what they say.

37

When frogs get up in the morning,
They always say, "Good day."

When frogs get up in the morning,
They always say, "Good day."

"Rib–bet, rib–bet,"
That is what they say, they say.

"Rib–bet, rib–bet,"
That is what they say.

Add a New Animal

Think of a new animal to put in this song. How does your animal say "Good day"?

Write about your new animal and the sound it makes. Draw a picture, too.

CITY PETS

Animal friends live in the city, too. See how many pets you can find on the following pages. How are these city pets different from the farm animals you have read about?

43

45

EAS

44

45

Poems about Animal Friends

THE LOST CAT

We can't find the cat,

We don't know where she's at,

Oh, where did she go?

Does anyone know?

Let's ask this walking hat.

by Shel Silverstein

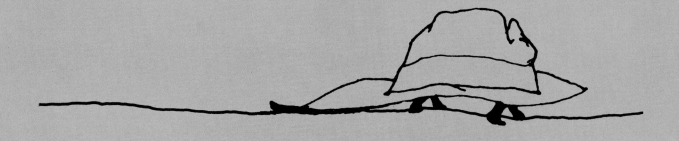

NOTICE

I have a dog,
I had a cat.
I've got a frog
Inside my hat.

by David McCord

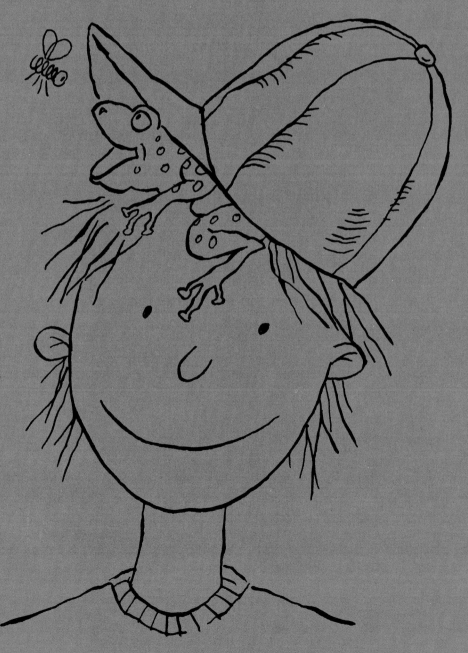

Dear Zoo

Rod Campbell

I wrote to the zoo

to send me a pet.

They sent me an...

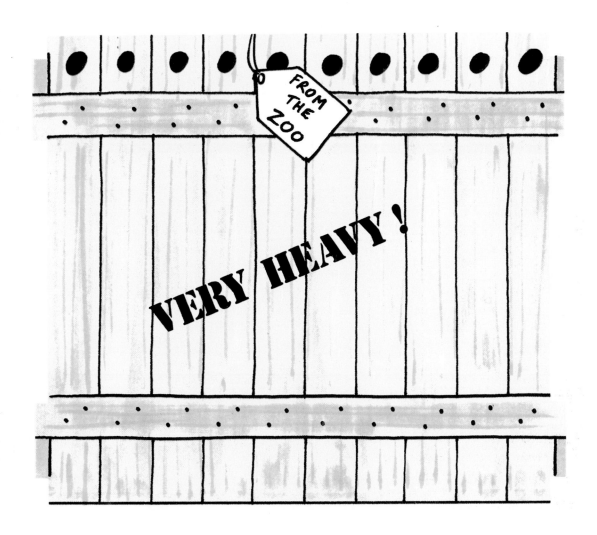

He was too big!
I sent him back.

So they sent me a...

He was too tall!
I sent him back.

So they sent me a ...

He was too fierce!
I sent him back.

So they sent me a ...

He was too grumpy!
I sent him back.

So they sent me a ...

He was too scary!
I sent him back.

So they sent me a ...

He was too naughty!
I sent him back.

So they sent me a ...

He was too jumpy!
I sent him back.

So they thought
very hard, and
sent me a ...

He was perfect!

I kept him.

Write a Letter

Do you think the zoo animals in the story would make good pets? Why or why not?

Think of an animal you would like for a pet. Then write a letter to a zoo, a farm, or a pet shop. Ask them to send you the animal.

Draw a picture to show why you would like to have this animal as a pet.

Dear Farm,

I want a pet. Please send me a chicken. Thank you. Yours truly,

Jessica

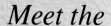

Author and Illustrator

Rod Campbell grew up in Africa. There, he saw many jungle animals. He wrote about those animals in *Dear Zoo*. He also drew the pictures for the book.

Mr. Campbell now lives in London, England.

At The Zoo

I've been to the zoo
   where the thing that you do
is watching the things
   that the animals do —

and watching
   the animals
   all watching
      you!

by Myra Cohn Livingston

67

ADOPT A

Skip to My Lou
by Nadine Bernard Westcott
You read this book together.
Now read it again. This time,
try singing it to a friend.

Four Black Puppies
by Sally Grindley
Could four sleeping puppies
cause a giant mess? What
will their owners think?

Where's Spot?

PET BOOK

A Children's Zoo
by Tana Hoban
What animal is striped black and white? The photographs in this book will help you name new animal friends.

Where's Spot?
by Eric Hill
You can help Spot's mother look for Spot by opening the flaps in this book. You'll be surprised!

Five Little Ducks
by Raffi
One by one, Mother Duck's children leave home. But when they come back, they have a nice surprise for Mother Duck!

69

BOOK 2

I can do it!

Big Book:
I Can't Get My Turtle to Move

The girl in this book can get all kinds of animals to do what she says. But when she tries to get a turtle to do things, it won't even move! Read this book together. Find out if the girl gets the turtle to move. Do you think she can do it?

You can do so many things! What did you do today that you couldn't do when you were a baby? What problems do you solve every day?

As you read these stories and poems, you will find out why each character might say, "I can do it!"

CONTENTS

Monster and the Baby

by Virginia Mueller
illustrated by Lynn Munsinger

74

I Wish I Could Fly

written and illustrated by Ron Maris

89

And So Can I!

by Bill Gillham

115

MONSTER AND THE BABY

by Virginia Mueller

illustrated by Lynn Munsinger

Baby was crying.

Monster gave Baby one red block.

Baby cried.

Monster gave Baby two yellow blocks.

Baby cried.

Monster gave Baby three blue blocks.

Baby cried.

Monster put the three blue blocks on the bottom,

the two yellow blocks in the middle,

and the one red block on the top.

Monster hit the blocks!

Baby laughed and laughed.

Monster Can Do It!

If Monster had no blocks, do you think he could still find a way to make Baby laugh?

Think of a new way to get Baby to stop crying. Draw a picture of Monster doing something funny or nice for Baby. Add speech balloons to show what Monster and Baby are saying.

The Wrong Start

I got up this morning and meant to be good,
But things didn't happen the way that they should.
    I lost my toothbrush,
       I slammed the door,
    I dropped an egg
       On the kitchen floor,
    I spilled some sugar
       And after that
    I tried to hurry
       And tripped on the cat.
Things may get better. I don't know when.
I think I'll go back and start over again.

by Marchette Chute

I Wish I Could Fly

by RON MARIS

"Good morning, Bird.

I wish I could fly like you."

CRASH! BANG!

WALLOP! CRUNCH!

"Hello, Frog.

I wish I could dive like you."

**FLOP! PLOP!
SPLUTTER! SPLASH!**

"How are you, Squirrel?
I wish I could climb like you."

WIBBLE! WOBBLE!
WRIGGLE! ROCK!

"Good day, Rabbit.

I wish I could run like you."

PUFF! PANT!
STAGGER! GASP!

"I can't fly like Bird,
I can't dive like Frog,
I can't climb like Squirrel,
I can't run like Rabbit, but . . ."

"When it rains,

I don't get wet.

I'm **SNUG**, **WARM**,

COZY, and **DRY**!"

I wish I could...

Are you like Turtle? Do you wish you could fly like a bird? Or climb like a squirrel? Think of something you wish you could do.

Draw a picture of it. Talk about your picture with some friends.

JUMP OR JIGGLE

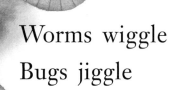

Frogs jump
Caterpillars hump

Worms wiggle
Bugs jiggle

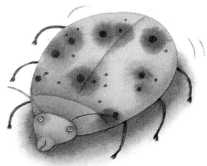

Rabbits hop
Horses clop

Snakes slide
Sea gulls glide

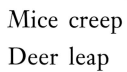

Mice creep
Deer leap

Puppies bounce
Kittens pounce

Lions stalk —
But —
I walk!

by Evelyn Beyer

111

I Speak, I Say, I Talk

Cats purr.

Lions roar.

Owls hoot.

Bears snore.

Crickets creak.

Mice squeak.

Sheep baa.

But I SPEAK!

Monkeys chatter.

Cows moo.

Ducks quack.

Doves coo.

Pigs squeal.

Horses neigh.

Chickens cluck.

But I SAY!

Flies hum.

Dogs growl.

Bats screech.

Coyotes howl.

Frogs croak.

Parrots squawk.

Bees buzz.

But I TALK!

by Arnold L. Shapiro

"I Speak, I Say, I Talk," by Arnold L. Shapiro, from *Poems and Rhymes*, Volume I of *Childcraft—The How and Why Library*. Copyright © 1984 by World Book, Inc.

And So Can I!

BILL GILLHAM

This dog can wade . . .

and so can I!

This pony can jump . . .

and so can I!

This pig can peek over a fence . . .

and so can I!

This rabbit can wash her face . . .

and so can I!

These little ducks can swim . . .

and so can I!

This donkey can eat an apple . . .

and so can I!

This hamster can climb a ladder . . .

and so can I!

This cat can lick . . .

and so can I!

This bird can hang on the bars . . .

and so can I!

But none of them . . .

can read a book like me!

And So Can You!

A pig can peek over a fence — and so can you! What other things can you do?

Draw a picture of yourself doing something you like. Draw a frame around your picture and write a sentence about it. Then put all the pictures together and help make a class picture album.

Meet the Authors and Illustrators

Virginia Mueller has four children. When they were babies, her children liked to play with blocks. This gave Mrs. Mueller the idea for *Monster and the Baby,* her first story about Monster.

Virginia Mueller is still writing stories — but now she gets ideas from her six grandchildren!

Lynn Munsinger was born in Massachusetts and went to art school there. When she finished school, Ms. Munsinger began to draw pictures for children's books. One of her recent storybooks is *One Hungry Monster.* She has also drawn pictures for *Cricket,* a magazine for children.

Ron Maris has written many books about animals. He drew the pictures for all of his books, including *I Wish I Could Fly*.

When he is not writing, Mr. Maris likes to help people learn to draw. He is now an art teacher at a school in England.

Bill Gillham was a teacher before he was a writer. He also used to fly an airplane.

Mr. Gillham likes to do many things, but most of all he likes writing books for children.

He now lives in Scotland.

I Can't Get My Turtle to Move

by Elizabeth Lee O'Donnell
You have read this counting book together. Now read it again. Can you count all the animals that appear in the story?

Bet You Can't

by Penny Dale
It's time to clean up and time for bed. This brother and sister make it time for fun, too!

The Chick and the Duckling

by Mirra Ginsburg
Each time the duckling tries something new, the chick says, "Me too." Will the chick change its mind?

You Can Read

Flap Your Wings and Try

by Charlotte Pomerantz

A baby bird learns to fly — but how? Find out what its secret is.

Molly Goes Hiking

by Ruth Radlauer

Molly wants to try out her new backpack. Follow her on a hiking adventure.

Max's Breakfast

by Rosemary Wells

Someone eats Max's egg. Is it Max?

Acknowledgments

For each of the selections listed below, grateful acknowledgment is made for permission to excerpt and/or reprint original or copyrighted material, as follows:

Major Selections

"And So Can I!" by Bill Gillham. Copyright © 1987 by Bill Gillham, excerpts reprinted by permission of G. P. Putnam's Sons, and Methuen Children's Books.

Dear Zoo, by Rod Campbell. Copyright © 1982 by Rod Campbell. Reprinted by permission of Macmillan Publishing Company, and Campbell Books Ltd. (*Dear Zoo* is published as a flap book.)

I Wish I Could Fly, by Ron Maris. Copyright © 1987 by Ron Maris. Reprinted by permission of Greenwillow Books (a division of William Morrow and Co.), and Julia MacRae Books.

Monster and the Baby, text copyright © 1985 by Virginia Mueller. Illustrations copyright © 1985 by Lynn Munsinger. Originally published in hardcover by Albert Whitman and Company. All rights reserved. Used with permission.

Who Is Tapping At My Window? by A. G. Deming, illustrated by Monica Wellington. Copyright © 1988 by Monica Wellington. Reprinted by permission of the publisher, Dutton Children's Books, a division of Penguin Books USA, Inc.

Poetry

"At The Zoo," from *Whispers and Other Poems*. Copyright © 1958 by Myra Cohn Livingston. Reprinted by permission of Marian Reiner for the author.

"I Speak, I Say, I Talk," by Arnold L. Shapiro, from *Once Upon A Time*, Volume 1 of *Childcraft—The How and Why Library*. Copyright © 1989 World Book, Inc. By permission of the publisher.

"Jump or Jiggle," by Evelyn Beyer from *Another Here and Now Storybook* by Lucy Sprague Mitchell. Copyright © 1937 by E. P. Dutton, Inc., renewed 1965 by Lucy Sprague Mitchell. Reprinted by permission.

"The Lost Cat," from *A Light In The Attic*, text and illustration by Shel Silverstein. Copyright © 1981 by Evil Eye Music, Inc. Reprinted by permission of Harper and Row, Publishers, Inc.

"Notice," from *One At A Time* by David McCord. Copyright © 1952 by David McCord. Reprinted by permission of Little, Brown and Company.

"The Wrong Start," from *Rhymes About Us* by Marchette Chute. Copyright © 1974 by E. P. Dutton, Inc. Reprinted by permission of Mary Chute Smith.

Read Along Books

The Read Along Books shown on pages 10, 68, 172, and 130 are available from Houghton Mifflin Company and are reprinted with permission from various publishers. Jacket artists for these books are listed below.

I Can't Get My Turtle to Move, by Elizabeth Lee O'Donnell. Jacket art by Maxie Chambliss, copyright © 1989 by Maxie Chambliss.

Skip to My Lou, by Nadine Bernard Westcott. Jacket art by Nadine Bernard Westcott copyright © 1989 by Nadine Bernard Westcott.

Additional Recommended Reading

Houghton Mifflin Company wishes to thank the following publishers for permission to reproduce their book covers on pages 68, 69, 130 and 131.

Greenwillow Books, a division of William Morrow & Company, Inc.:
A Children's Zoo, by Tana Hoban. Jacket photograph by Tana Hoban, copyright © 1985 by Tana Hoban.

J. B. Lippincott Junior Books, a subsidiary of Harper & Row, Publishers, Inc.:
Bet You Can't, by Penny Dale. Jacket art by Penny Dale, copyright © 1987 by Penny Dale. First published in England by Walker Books Limited, London.

Lothrop, Lee & Shepherd Books, a division of William Morrow & Company, Inc.:
Four Black Puppies, by Sally Grindley. Jacket art by Clive Scruton, copyright © 1987 by Clive Scruton. First published in Great Britain in 1987 by Walker Books Limited.

Macmillan Publishing Company:
The Chick and the Duckling, by Mirra Ginsburg. Cover jacket art by Jose Aruego, copyright © 1972 by Jose Aruego.

G. P. Putnam's Sons, a division of the Putnam Publishing Group:
Where's Spot? by Eric Hill. Jacket art by Eric Hill, copyright © 1980 by Eric Hill. Published simultaneously in Canada by General Publishing Company Limited, Toronto.

Troubadour Learning, Inc.:
Five Little Ducks, Raffi Songs to Read™. Jacket art by Jose Aruego and Ariane Dewey, copyright © 1989 by Jose Aruego and Ariane Dewey.

Credits

Program design   Carbone Smolan Associates

Cover design   Carbone Smolan Associates

Design   8–69 Carbone Smolan Associates;   **70–131**
Pronk&Associates

Illustrations   8–11 Ajin Noda;   **12–28** Monica
Wellington;   **29** Ajin Noda;   **30–40** Felicia Bond;   **41–45**
Fritz Karch;   **46** Shel Silverstein;   **47** Ellen Sasaki;   **48–64**
Rod Campbell;   **65** Mary Lynn Blasutta;   **66** Ajin Noda;
67 Don Stuart;   **68–69** Mary Lynn Blasutta;   **72**
Pronk&Associates;   **74–87** Lynn Munsinger;   **88** Kim La
Fave;   **89–108** Ron Maris;   **110–111** Don Stuart;   **112–
114** Julie Koontz;   **128–129** Pronk&Associates

Photography   41 A. Matoba/Superstock;   **42** (top) Kindra
Clineff, (bottom) Superstock;   **43** Superstock;   **44** (top)
Kindra Clineff, (center & bottom) Superstock;   **45** (top) A.
Matoba/Superstock, (right) Herbert Schwind/Okadia/Photo
Researchers, (bottom) Superstock;   **70** David Vance/The
Image Bank (top left); Rommel/Masterfile (top right),
Stephen Marks/Stockphotos, Inc. (bottom);   **71** Andrew
McKim/Masterfile (top right) Michael Rosenfeld/The Image
Bank (lower left); Elyse Lewin/The Image Bank (lower right);
109 See Spot Run;   **130–131** Ian Chrysler